WeightWatchers®

Discover Plan

Italia

60 new and satisfying Italian recipes developed for the Discover Plan™

Ideal for the whole family

Penny Stephens

SIMON & SCHUSTER
A CBS COMPANY

First published in Great Britain by Simon & Schuster UK Ltd, 2009
A CBS Company

Copyright © 2009, Weight Watchers International, Inc.

Simon & Schuster UK Ltd, 1st Floor, 222 Gray's Inn Road,
London WC1X 8HB

Weight Watchers and **POINTS** are the registered trademarks of
Weight Watchers International Inc. **Discover Plan** is a trademark of
Weight Watchers International Inc., and all are used under its control
by Weight Watchers (UK) Ltd.

Weight Watchers Publications Team Jane Griffiths, Donna Watts,
Nina McKerlie and Fiona Smith
Simon and Schuster Project Editor Anna Hitchin
Photography by Steve Baxter
Styling by Rachel Jukes
Food preparation and styling by Penny Stephens
Design and typesetting by Jane Humphrey

Printed and bound in China

A CIP catalogue for this book is available from the British Library

Pictured on the back cover: Top right: Pizza Bianco, page 27;
Top to bottom on the left: Grissini, page 7; Giant Shells with Spinach
and Basil Pesto, page 24; Zabaglione with Raspberries, page 59.

Pictured on page 4: Roasted Butternut Squash Risotto with Gorgonzola
and Sage, page 21.

 POINTS® value logo: You'll find this easy to read **POINTS** value logo on every recipe throughout this book. The logo represents the number of **POINTS** values per serving each recipe contains. Weight Watchers **POINTS** system is a simple way to lose weight. As part of the Weight Watchers Discover Plan™ you'll enjoy eating delicious, healthy, filling foods that help keep you feeling satisfied for longer and in control of both your portion sizes and your hunger.

Filling Foods are highlighted in green – like this. Focus on these foods where you can – they keep you feeling satisfied for longer.

Ⓥ This symbol denotes a vegetarian recipe and assumes that, where relevant, free range eggs, vegetarian cheese, vegetarian virtually fat free fromage frais and vegetarian low fat crème fraîche are used. Virtually fat free fromage frais and low fat crème fraîche may contain traces of gelatine so they are not always vegetarian. Please check the labels.

❅ This symbol denotes a dish that can be frozen.

Recipe notes

Egg size Medium, unless otherwise stated.
All fruits and vegetables Medium size unless otherwise stated.
Raw eggs Only the freshest eggs should be used. Pregnant women, the elderly and children should avoid recipes with eggs which are not fully cooked or raw.
Recipe timings These are approximate and meant to be guidelines. Please note that the preparation time includes all the steps up to and following the main cooking time(s).
Polyunsaturated margarine Use brands such as Flora Light, St Ivel Gold and Benecol Light.
Stock Stock cubes should be used in the recipes, unless otherwise stated. Prepare them according to the packet instructions.

contents

Italian is the fantastic new cookbook from Weight Watchers. It's packed with 60 mouth-watering recipes that are sure to bring some Mediterranean flair into your kitchen.

In *Italian* you will find superb recipes for pastas, risottos, pizzas, fish and meat dishes as well as tempting soups and salads – and desserts of course – all developed to help you stay satisfied and in control as you lose weight.

The recipes range from classic Italian favourites such as Tuscan Onion Soup, Gnocchi with Fresh Tomato Sauce, Saltimbocca and Zabaglione with Raspberries to more contemporary recipes like Roasted Pepper Soup with Parmesan Crisps, Capri Salad, Risotto Verde, Pizza Bianco and Strawberry and Vanilla Panna Cotta. With such a wide variety of satisfying Italian culinary delights to choose from, you'll never be short of ideas for lunch, supper or dessert. And all the recipes are low in **POINTS**® values too.

Developed to work alongside the Discover Plan™, *Italian* can help you to stretch your **POINTS** allowance since many of the recipes contain **Filling Foods**.

Filling Foods can help you get the most from your **POINTS** values so you can eat more and make your daily allowance go even further. You'll easily be able to identify the **Filling Foods** used in these recipes since they are highlighted in green.

Each recipe has the **POINTS** values per serving clearly marked so you can easily track what you are eating and stay within your **POINTS** allowance.

Boun Appetito

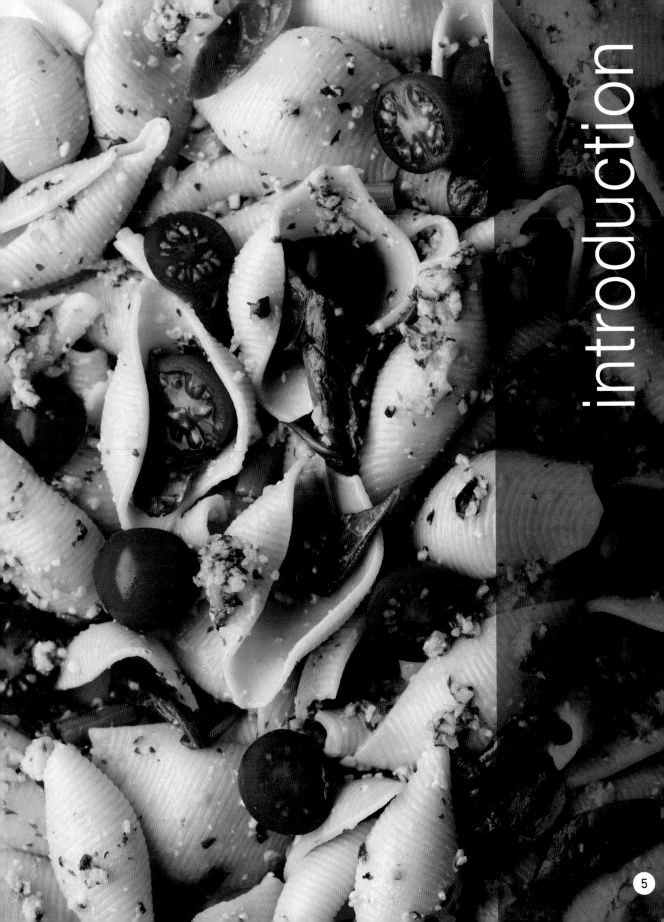

grissini

*For an extra **POINTS** value of ½ per serving, cut a 12 g slice of Parma ham in half and wrap it around the top of each grissini.*

Ⓨ *Makes **15** • Takes **15** minutes to prepare + rising, **20** minutes to cook • **8 POINTS** values per recipe • **31** calories per serving*

110 g (4 oz) strong white flour, plus 1 tablespoon for dusting
1 tablespoon semolina, plus 1 tablespoon for dusting
½ teaspoon easy blend dried yeast
1 teaspoon extra virgin olive oil
salt and freshly ground black pepper

❶ Sift the flour into a large bowl, add the semolina and yeast and mix well, stirring in a little seasoning. Add the oil and 50–75 ml (2–3 fl oz) hand hot water. Bring the mixture together to form a dough. Dust the surface with the extra tablespoon of flour, turn the dough out and knead for a few minutes until smooth and stretchy. Return to the bowl, cover with a clean cloth and leave to rise for 5 minutes.

❷ Preheat the oven to Gas Mark 7/220°C/fan oven 200°C. Roll out the dough to about 25 x 15 cm (10 x 6 inches) and cut into 12 thin strips. Twist each one slightly. Sprinkle a non stick baking tray with a little semolina to prevent the grissini from sticking, and place the strips on it. Leave to rise for 15–20 minutes.

❸ Bake for 10 minutes then reduce the oven temperature to Gas Mark 1/140°C/fan oven 120°C, leaving the oven door open for a minute to allow it to cool down more quickly. Close the door and leave in the oven for a further 10 minutes to dry out. Remove from the oven, cool and store in an airtight container, for up to 2 days.

Serving suggestion *To serve with a zero **POINTS** value salsa, chop and de-seed 4 medium vine tomatoes and mix with ½ a finely diced red onion, 1 tablespoon of capers, 1 tablespoon of chopped parsley and 1 tablespoon of white wine vinegar.*

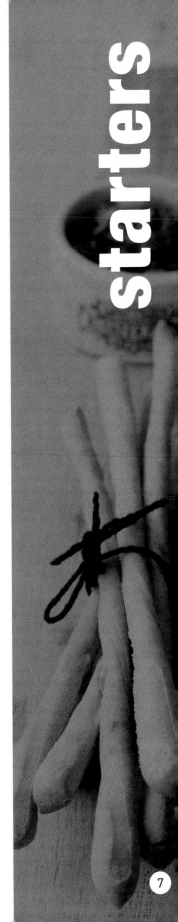

Enjoy robust flavours in these delicious and satisfying starters or light lunches.

starters

vegetable and anchovy rolls

You can vary the ingredients – try a little chilli, chopped ham or olives in brine, remembering to add the extra **POINTS** values.

Makes **10** • Takes **30** minutes to prepare + rising, **15** minutes to cook • **10 POINTS** values per recipe • **62** calories per serving

145 g packet pizza dough mix
low fat cooking spray
½ red pepper, de-seeded and diced
1 small red onion, diced
1 small courgette, diced
1 vine ripened tomato, chopped roughly
1 tablespoon thyme leaves
a handful of basil leaves
15 g (½ oz) canned anchovies in oil, rinsed, drained and chopped
1 tablespoon tomato purée
1 tablespoon flour, for dusting

❶ Make up the pizza dough following the packet instructions. Leave to rise for 10 minutes. Preheat the oven to Gas Mark 5/190°C/fan oven 170°C.
❷ Spray a large, non stick frying pan with the cooking spray and heat until hot. Add the pepper, onion and courgette. Stir fry for 5 minutes, adding a little water if it starts to stick. Add the tomato and thyme and cook for a further 5 minutes. Stir in the basil, anchovies and tomato purée. Set aside.
❸ On a surface lightly dusted with flour, roll out the dough to a 30 x 20 cm (12 x 8 inch) rectangle. Spread over the vegetable mixture evenly. Roll up from one long side. Slice into 10 rounds. Place on a baking tray lined with non stick baking parchment. Bake for 15 minutes until golden.

Tip Keep in an airtight container in the fridge for up to 3 days.

Goes well with...
The Tuscan Onion Soup on page 10, instead of the ciabatta, for no extra **POINTS** values per serving.

olive dip with melba toast

This is a richly flavoured olive pâté, made with classic Mediterranean ingredients. Serve as a starter or as a canapé with drinks.

Ⓥ Serves **4** • Takes **5** minutes • **5½ POINTS** values per recipe • **73** calories per serving

110 g (4 oz) pitted black olives in brine, drained
50 g (1¾ oz) low fat soft cheese
1 tablespoon capers in brine, rinsed
1 tablespoon chopped fresh parsley
squeeze of lemon juice
2 slices medium white bread
freshly ground black pepper

❶ To make the dip, place the olives in a food processor and blitz to a rough paste. Add the soft cheese and capers and blend again. Remove to a bowl and stir in the parsley and lemon juice. Season with black pepper but taste before adding any salt as the olives will probably make it salty enough. Cover and chill until required.
❷ To make the melba toast, preheat the grill to medium and toast the bread on one side. Cut off the crusts and carefully slice the toast in half horizontally to make two thin slices. Cut each thin slice into four triangles and toast the uncooked side until golden.
❸ Serve the dip in a small pot (an egg cup is ideal) with four triangles of toast each.

Variations You can make the dip with green olives, instead of black, for a slightly milder flavour. The **POINTS** values will remain the same.

Try adding 1 teaspoon of finely diced red chilli with the parsley for a spicy version.

For a canapé, spoon the mixture on to the toasts and garnish each with a sprig of parsley to hand round to guests.

roasted pepper soup with Parmesan crisps

Ⓥ *Serves* **4** • *Takes* **10** *minutes to prepare*, **35** *minutes to cook* • **6½ POINTS** *values per recipe* • **153** *calories per serving*

6 red peppers**, de-seeded and sliced**

3 garlic cloves

2 teaspoons olive oil

2 sprigs of fresh rosemary**, needles only**

1 litre (1¾ pints) hot vegetable stock

For the crisps

8 teaspoons freshly grated Parmesan cheese

2 teaspoons thyme **leaves**

freshly ground black pepper

❶ Preheat the oven to Gas Mark 6/200°C/fan oven 180°C. Line a baking tin with foil, add the peppers and whole garlic cloves. Drizzle over the oil and add the rosemary, tossing to cover the vegetables. Roast for 30 minutes until softened and lightly charred. Remove the tray, leaving the oven on. Pop the garlic from their skins.

❷ Place the peppers and garlic, and their juices, in a large saucepan with about a third of the stock. Use a hand blender to blitz the soup until roughly smooth. Return to the pan, add the remaining stock and heat through until hot.

❸ Meanwhile, mix together the grated Parmesan with the thyme and a little black pepper. Place teaspoons of the mixture, well spaced apart, on a non stick baking tray, making eight piles. There is no need to push them down. Bake for 5 minutes until golden. Leave to cool on the tray for a few minutes before carefully transferring to a plate. The cheese spreads as it melts and cooks to look like a crisp with little holes.

❹ Serve the soup in warm bowls with two Parmesan crisps each.

Tips *You can use a variety of coloured peppers in this soup although red, orange and yellow are the best since they are sweeter.*

If your baking tray is not non stick, use non stick baking parchment or a Teflon sheet on top.

Tuscan onion soup

This is richly warming with a fabulous flavour coming from the lightly caramelised onions. If you serve the soup without the ciabatta, the *POINTS* values will be zero per serving.

Ⓥ *Serves* **2** • *Takes* **5** *minutes to prepare*, **35** *minutes to cook* • **3** *POINTS values per recipe* • **174** *calories per serving*

low fat cooking spray
2 large onions, sliced thinly
1 sprig of fresh rosemary
1 sprig of fresh oregano or 1 teaspoon dried oregano
1 garlic clove, crushed
500 ml (18 fl oz) hot vegetable stock
salt and freshly ground black pepper
2 x 40 g (1½ oz) slices ciabatta, to serve

❶ Spray a large, lidded saucepan with the cooking spray and heat until hot. Add the onions and stir fry over a high heat for 3 minutes. Add the herbs and garlic and reduce the heat to low. Cover the onions with a piece of baking parchment so that it actually touches them, then cover the pan with a lid. Leave them undisturbed for 20 minutes. If you leave them on a low heat, they won't stick.

❷ Stir, cover again with the paper and the lid and cook for another 10 minutes. The onions should be silky, very soft and a light golden colour. Remove the herb stems, pulling off any remaining leaves and putting them back in the pan. Discard the stems.

❸ Add the stock to the onions and slowly bring to the boil. Season and serve in warmed bowls with the bread on the side.

Tip *Oregano has a similar flavour to marjoram. Fresh oregano has a small, slightly furry leaf which can be added whole to dishes.*

chunky vegetable and salami soup

Similar to a minestrone, this soup is almost like a stew. It's packed with vegetables and pasta and garnished with tasty strips of salami.

❄ *Serves* **4** • *Takes* **10** *minutes to prepare*, **25** *minutes to cook* • **8½** *POINTS values per recipe* • **175** *calories per serving*

low fat cooking spray
1 onion, diced
2 carrots, peeled and diced
2 celery sticks, diced
1 garlic clove, crushed
60 g (2 oz) small pasta shapes
400 g can chopped tomatoes
600 ml (20 fl oz) hot vegetable stock
110 g (4 oz) spinach leaves
75 g (2¾ oz) salami, cut into thin strips
salt and freshly ground black pepper
a handful of basil leaves, to garnish

❶ Spray a large, lidded saucepan with the cooking spray and heat until hot. Add the onion, carrots and celery. Stir fry for 5 minutes, adding a little water if the mixture starts to stick. Stir in the garlic and cook for a minute.

❷ Add the pasta, tomatoes and stock. Bring to the boil, cover and simmer for 15 minutes until all the vegetables and pasta are tender. Remove from the heat and stir in the spinach. Season to taste. Cover and leave to let the spinach wilt.

❸ Meanwhile, heat a small, non stick frying pan until hot. Add the strips of salami and cook over a high heat for 1–2 minutes until crispy. Drain on kitchen paper.

❹ Serve the soup in large bowls. Sprinkle over the salami and garnish with the basil leaves.

Variation *Cavolo nero is a fabulous green winter vegetable and a great alternative to spinach. Chop and add in step 2 for the final 5 minutes of cooking time, for the same POINTS values per serving.*

Capri salad

This warm tomato and mozzarella stack is easy to assemble and makes an impressive supper party starter.

Serves **4** • *Takes* **15** *minutes* • **9½ POINTS** *values per recipe* • **104** *calories per serving*

4 beef steak **tomatoes**

125 g packet soft mozzarella light, cut into 8
    slices, each slice halved

50 g (1¾ oz) black or green **olives in brine**,
    drained and sliced

2 tablespoons **capers in brine**, rinsed

12 **basil** leaves, plus extra to garnish

2 tablespoons balsamic vinegar

salt and freshly ground black pepper

❶ Preheat the grill to medium. Cut thin slices from the top and bottom of each tomato and discard, then slice each tomato horizontally into four slices.

❷ Line a grill pan with foil. Place a slice of tomato on the foil, top with a slice of mozzarella, scatter over a few olive slices, a few capers and a basil leaf and season. Finish with a slice of mozzarella. Repeat the layers described above and make four stacks in total, starting with a tomato slice and ending with a slice of mozzarella on the top. Grill for 2–5 minutes until warm and the cheese has begun to melt.

❸ Serve each stack drizzled with ½ a tablespoon of balsamic vinegar and garnished with basil leaves.

Variations *If you prefer, you can simply arrange the ingredients on a plate instead of making stacks, and enjoy it as a cold salad.*

Fresh **oregano** *or* **thyme**, *together or separately, work well as alternatives to the* **basil**.

stuffed courgettes

The small courgettes are best for this dish as they tend to be sweeter and look nice too.

Serves 2 • Takes 15 minutes to prepare, 30–40 minutes to cook • 4½ POINTS values per recipe • 173 calories per serving

2 small courgettes, trimmed and halved
    lengthways
15 g sun-dried tomatoes, reconstituted according
    to packet instructions
40 g (1½ oz) ciabatta breadcrumbs (see tip)
1 teaspoon dried oregano
1 garlic clove, crushed
1 tablespoon pine nut kernels
15 g (½ oz) low fat polyunsaturated margarine
low fat cooking spray
salt and freshly ground black pepper
a handful of basil leaves, to garnish

❶ Preheat the oven to Gas Mark 5/190°C/fan oven 170°C. Using a teaspoon, scoop the middle seeds from the courgette halves, discard and place the halves in a snug fitting ovenproof dish. Season the courgettes. Drain the tomatoes, reserving 6 tablespoons of the liquid and cut the tomatoes into thin strips.

❷ Mix together the ciabatta breadcrumbs, tomatoes, oregano, garlic, pine nut kernels and margarine. Season lightly. Divide the mixture between the courgettes and spray with the cooking spray. Pour the reserved tomato liquid around the courgettes. Bake for 30–40 minutes until the courgettes are just tender and the topping is golden. Garnish with the basil leaves before serving.

Tip *To make the ciabatta breadcrumbs, whizz chunks of the ciabatta in a food processor or mini blender. Alternatively, you can use the equivalent weight in wholemeal breadcrumbs, for the same POINTS values per serving.*

piadina

Serves 4 • Takes 15 minutes • 13 POINTS values per recipe • 235 calories per serving

1 small aubergine, sliced into rounds
1 small courgette, sliced thinly lengthways
3 artichoke hearts from a can, drained and halved
low fat cooking spray
2 plum tomatoes, sliced
75 g (2¾ oz) soft mozzarella light, sliced
4 x 50 g multigrain tortilla wraps (about
    20 cm /8 inches in diameter)
a handful of basil leaves
salt and freshly ground black pepper

❶ Heat a ridged griddle pan or non stick frying pan until hot. Spray the aubergine, courgette and artichokes with the cooking spray and cook them in batches, turning once until charred and softened. Keep warm while you cook all the batches.

❷ Arrange the vegetables, tomatoes and mozzarella between two of the wraps. Scatter over the basil and season. Top with the other two wraps, press down and spray the top with the cooking spray. Carefully turn over, placing the sprayed side on the griddle or frying pan.

❸ Cook for 1 minute. Spray the top with the cooking spray. Using a wide spatula, turn it over. Cook for 1 minute. Remove from the pan. Cut into quarters and serve two quarters each.

Parma ham and chick pea salad

Serve this salad warm or leave it to cool and allow the flavours to develop.

Serves **1** • *Takes* **15** *minutes* • **3** *POINTS values per recipe* • **241** *calories per serving*

low fat cooking spray
1 small red onion, sliced thinly
6 cherry tomatoes
1 garlic clove, crushed
½ x 400 g can chick peas, drained
2 sprigs of fresh thyme, leaves only
2 x 12 g slices Parma ham, cut into strips
1 tablespoon balsamic vinegar
a handful of rocket leaves, to serve (optional)

❶ Spray a medium size, non stick frying pan with the cooking spray and heat until hot. Add the onion and cook, stirring for 5 minutes. Add the tomatoes and garlic. Continue cooking for a further 2–3 minutes until the onion slices are tender and the tomatoes are beginning to split.

❷ Add all the remaining ingredients, except the rocket, with a splash of water and stir fry for a minute. The salad should be just warm. Serve warm as it is, or cool and chill, and serve with rocket leaves (if using).

Variation *This works well with half a can of pinto or flageolet beans in place of the chick peas, for the same POINTS values per serving.*

Sicilian steak salad

Serves **4** • *Takes* **20** *minutes + marinating* • **13½** *POINTS values per recipe* • **211** *calories per serving*

2 small sprigs of fresh rosemary, needles only
1 tablespoon roughly chopped fresh parsley
juice of ½ a lemon
400 g (14 oz) sirloin steak, trimmed of visible fat
25 g (1 oz) pine nut kernels
25 g (1 oz) raisins
75 ml (3 fl oz) balsamic vinegar
85 g bag watercress
1 Little Gem lettuce, shredded
8 cherry tomatoes, halved
salt and freshly ground black pepper

❶ Roughly crush the rosemary in a mortar and pestle, mixing in the parsley and lemon juice. Season the steak on both sides, then smear the rough paste over the meat. Cover and set aside to marinate for 20 minutes.

❷ Meanwhile, toast the pine nut kernels in a small, non stick frying pan over a medium heat, stirring regularly for a minute or so until they are golden. Remove from the pan and set aside.

❸ Heat the same frying pan until hot, add the steak and cook for 2–3 minutes, turning once. If you like your steak well done, cook for 5–6 minutes. Remove from the pan to a plate and cover with foil to rest and keep warm.

❹ Return the pan to the heat. Add the raisins and the balsamic vinegar, which will sizzle. Swirl to deglaze the pan and loosen any meat bits, then reduce the heat and simmer for a minute or two until slightly syrupy.

❺ To serve, divide the watercress, lettuce and tomatoes between four plates. Slice the steak and place on top. Scatter over the pine nut kernels and drizzle over the balsamic raisins.

Variation *You can replace the pine nut kernels with the same quantity of sunflower seeds, for the same POINTS values per serving.*

lamb bruschetta

Bruschetta is garlic rubbed toast and can be used as a base for lots of dishes. Here it is topped with a great combination of pan fried strips of tender lamb, mushrooms and sun-dried tomatoes.

Serves **2** • *Takes* **15** *minutes* • **6½** *POINTS values per recipe* • **190** *calories per serving*

low fat cooking spray
125 g (4½ oz) lean lamb leg steak, cut into thin
   strips
1 onion, sliced
75 g (2¾ oz) mushrooms, chopped
25 g (1 oz) sun-dried tomatoes in oil, drained
1 sprig of fresh rosemary, needles only
4 x 10 g (¼ oz) slices ciabatta
1 garlic clove, left whole

❶ Spray a non stick frying pan with the cooking spray and heat until hot. Add the lamb, onion and mushrooms and stir fry for 3 minutes. Add the sun-dried tomatoes and rosemary. Continue cooking until the lamb is just brown. Add 2 tablespoons of water, reduce the heat and simmer for 2 minutes.

❷ Meanwhile, preheat the grill to medium and toast the ciabatta on one side. Remove from the grill and immediately rub the garlic clove vigorously over the toasted side of each slice. Discard the garlic.

❸ To serve, top each toast with the hot lamb mixture, dividing equally.

Ⓥ **Variation** *For a vegetarian version, you can use 75 g (2¾ oz) Quorn Chicken Style Pieces, instead of the lamb, for a POINTS value of 2½ per serving.*

gnocchi with fresh tomato sauce

Serves **4** • Takes **20** *minutes to prepare + cooling,*
15 *minutes to cook* • **8½ POINTS** *values per recipe*
• **162** *calories per serving*

350 g (12 oz) floury potatoes, such as Désirée,
    peeled and chopped
75 g (2¾ oz) self raising flour, plus 1 tablespoon
    for dusting
2 teaspoons dried mixed herbs
salt and freshly ground black pepper
For the sauce
low fat cooking spray
1 onion, chopped
1 garlic clove, chopped
450 g (1 lb) plum tomatoes, chopped
a large handful of basil leaves

❶ Bring a large, lidded pan of water to the boil.
Add the potatoes, cover and simmer for 10–15
minutes until tender. Drain and mash. Stir in the
flour and herbs with a little seasoning. Set aside.
❷ Meanwhile, spray a saucepan with the cooking
spray and heat until hot. Add the onions and
cook for 3 minutes before adding the garlic and
tomatoes. Simmer, uncovered, for 10 minutes until
pulpy. Season and stir in half the basil.
❸ Bring a large pan of water to the boil. Dust the
work surface with the extra 1 tablespoon of flour
and shape the potato into long thin sausages about
2.5 cm (1 inch) in diameter. Cut off 2.5 cm (1 inch)
lengths. Rest the gnocchi on your finger and then
press the prongs of a fork on to one side of the
gnocchi. Add the gnocchi to the pan and cook in
batches for 2–3 minutes. They should rise to the
surface when ready. Use a slotted spoon to remove
from the pan to warm serving plates and keep
warm while you cook the rest.
❹ Spoon the sauce over the gnocchi and serve
with the remaining basil.

Easy, delicious
and truly Italian,
you'll be spoilt
for choice with
these recipes
which are ideal
for a leisurely
lunch or dinner.

pizza and pasta

roasted vegetable cannelloni

*Serve with a large zero **POINTS** value green salad.*

Ⓥ ❄ *Serves **4** • Takes **20** minutes to prepare,*
1 hour–1 hour 10 *minutes to cook* • **11 POINTS**
values per recipe • **286** *calories per serving*

1 large onion, **diced**
2 small courgettes, **diced**
1 aubergine, **trimmed and diced**
1 red pepper, **de-seeded and diced**
1 yellow pepper, **de-seeded and diced**
4 garlic cloves, **left whole**
1 sprig of fresh rosemary
low fat cooking spray
700 g jar passata
2 teaspoons dried mixed herbs
16 cannelloni tubes **(approx 160 g total weight)**
25 g (1 oz) Parmesan cheese, grated finely
salt and freshly ground black pepper

❶ Preheat the oven to Gas Mark 6/200°C/fan
oven 180°C. Place all the vegetables, garlic and
the rosemary in a large roasting tin, in one layer if
possible and spray with the cooking spray. Roast
for 30 minutes until softened and lightly charred.
Remove from the oven and reduce the temperature
to Gas Mark 4/180°C/fan oven 160°C.

❷ Remove the garlic from the roasted vegetables
and pop them from their skins into a small pan.
Add the passata and mixed herbs and warm gently.
Season.

❸ Add 6 tablespoons of the passata mixture to the
vegetables and stir to coat. Fill the pasta tubes with
the vegetables and lay in one layer in an ovenproof
dish. Pour over the remaining passata, ensuring all
the tubes are covered. Sprinkle over the Parmesan
cheese and place on a baking tray. Bake for 30–40
minutes until the pasta is cooked through and the
top is golden.

Tip *Although the vegetables will shrink a little when
roasted, remember to chop them small enough to fit
inside the pasta tubes.*

creamy tomato macaroni

*You can prepare the sauce ahead of time and then
assemble and bake it after work.*

Ⓥ *Serves **4** • Takes **20** minutes to prepare, **35–40***
minutes to cook • **16½ POINTS** *values per recipe*
• **303** *calories per serving*

low fat cooking spray
1 red onion, **chopped**
1 garlic clove, **crushed**
2 x 400 g cans chopped tomatoes
2 sprigs of fresh thyme
300 ml (10 fl oz) hot vegetable stock
3 tablespoons low fat soft cheese
2 tablespoons tomato purée
a pinch of sugar
225 g (8 oz) macaroni
salt and freshly ground black pepper
To serve
a handful of basil **leaves, to garnish**
50 g (1¾ oz) low fat grated Cheddar cheese

❶ Spray a medium, deep, non stick frying pan with
the cooking spray. Heat until hot. Add the onion.
Cook for 5 minutes until softened, adding a little
water if it starts to stick. Add the garlic and cook for
a further minute, then stir in the tomatoes, thyme
and stock. Reduce the heat and simmer for 10
minutes. Remove from the heat and blend using a
hand blender, or transfer to a liquidiser, and blend
until smooth. Stir in the soft cheese, tomato purée
and sugar. Season.

❷ Place the pasta in a lidded ovenproof dish and
pour over the sauce. Mix well and bake for 35–40
minutes until tender. Serve garnished with basil
leaves and sprinkled with the grated cheese.

Variation *For a smoky flavour, add ½ a teaspoon of
smoked paprika with the garlic in step 1.*

Goes well with...
*The Stuffed Courgettes on page 13 (remembering to
double the quantities for four people), for an extra
2½ **POINTS** values per serving.*

crab and coriander linguine

This is a lovely, fresh tasting pasta dish which would be good for supper with friends or as a midweek family meal.

Serves **4** • Takes **5** minutes to prepare, **10** minutes to cook • **15 POINTS** values per recipe • **268** calories per serving

250 g (9 oz) linguine
finely grated zest of 1 lime and the juice of 2 limes
2 x 170 g cans white crab meat in brine, drained
10 cherry tomatoes, halved
3 tablespoons chopped fresh coriander
1 red chilli, de-seeded and diced
salt and freshly ground black pepper

❶ Bring a large pan of water to the boil, add the pasta and cook according to the packet instructions. Drain, reserving 4 tablespoons of the cooking liquid and return both to the pan.

❷ Reserving a little coriander and chilli to garnish, add the remaining ingredients, tossing well to combine. Season and serve in warm bowls.

Variation This could be made using the same amount of canned tuna in brine or spring water, instead of the crab meat. The **POINTS** values will be the same.

risotto verde

Green and gorgeous, this creamy risotto is full of lovely herbs and fresh green vegetables.

Serves **4** • Takes **30** *minutes* • **15½ POINTS** *values per recipe* • **290** *calories per serving*

low fat cooking spray
300 g (10½ oz) risotto rice
150 g (5½ oz) green beans, trimmed
    and cut into 5 cm (2 inch) lengths
1.2 litres (2 pints) hot vegetable stock
150 g (5½ oz) chopped frozen spinach
2 tablespoons chopped fresh parsley
1 tablespoon chopped fresh dill
finely grated zest and juice of 1 lemon

❶ Spray a large, non stick frying pan with the cooking spray and heat until hot. Add the rice and beans and cook, stirring for 1 minute until the rice is opaque. Add a ladleful of stock, let it bubble and be absorbed before adding more, a little at a time. Stir occasionally until all the stock is used and the rice is tender.
❷ Stir in the spinach and once defrosted, add the herbs. Warm over a gentle heat until hot, then add the lemon zest and juice. Serve in warm bowls.

Variation *You can use the same amount of broccoli, instead of beans, but you will need to steam the florets in step 1 and add to the risotto at the last minute in step 2. The **POINTS** values will remain the same.*

sausage and fennel pasta

Fennel has a light aniseed flavour and is used in a lot of Italian recipes. It can also be used raw in salad and pasta dishes.

Serves **4** • Takes **25** *minutes* • **19½ POINTS** *values per recipe* • **338** *calories per serving*

400 g pack of 6 Weight Watchers Premium
    Pork Sausages
200 g (7 oz) wholemeal penne pasta
low fat cooking spray
1 onion, diced
1 fennel bulb, sliced thinly
198 g can sweetcorn, drained
finely grated zest of 1 small lemon

❶ Preheat the grill to medium and cook the sausages for 10–15 minutes turning regularly, until brown and cooked through.
❷ At the same time, bring a large pan of water to the boil. Add the pasta and cook according to the packet instructions. Drain, reserving 4 tablespoons of the cooking liquid.
❸ Meanwhile, spray a medium, non stick frying pan with the cooking spray and heat until hot. Add the onion and fennel and stir fry for 4 minutes until just tender.
❹ Return the pasta to the pan with the reserved cooking liquid, onion and fennel mixture and sweetcorn. Chop the sausages into bite size pieces. Add to the pan with the lemon zest. Heat through gently until piping hot.

Ⓨ **Variation** *For a vegetarian version, use a 250 g pack of Quorn sausages, instead of the pork sausages. The **POINTS** values will be 4 per serving.*

roasted butternut squash risotto with gorgonzola and sage

Butternut squash is deliciously sweet and goes well with a piquant cheese such as gorgonzola.

Ⓥ *Serves* **4** • *Takes* **35** *minutes* • **20½** *POINTS values per recipe* • **364** *calories per serving*

450 g (1 lb) butternut squash**, peeled, de-seeded and chopped into even, medium size chunks**
4 garlic cloves**, skins on**
low fat cooking spray
10 sage leaves
300 g (10½ oz) risotto rice
1.2 litres (2 pints) hot vegetable stock
60 g (2 oz) gorgonzola, crumbled
salt and freshly ground black pepper

❶ Preheat the oven to Gas Mark 6/200°C/fan oven 180°C. Place the squash and garlic cloves in a roasting tin, spray with the cooking spray and roast for 25 minutes. Stir the squash, add eight of the sage leaves, spray again with the cooking spray, stir and continue cooking for another 10 minutes until the squash is tender and lightly charred.

❷ Meanwhile, spray a large, non stick frying pan with the cooking spray and heat until hot. Add the rice and stir fry for 1 minute. Finely chop the remaining two sage leaves and add to the pan with a ladleful of stock. Let it bubble and be absorbed before adding more, a little at a time. Once the stock has been absorbed, continue adding a ladleful at a time. Stir occasionally until all the stock has been used and the rice is tender.

❸ To serve, set aside the roasted sage leaves, remove the garlic cloves and pop them from their skins. Stir the softened garlic flesh into the risotto together with the squash. Season and warm through over a low heat until piping hot. Add a little water if it becomes too dry. Stir in the gorgonzola at the last minute and serve garnished with the roasted sage leaves.

Variation *Most blue cheeses will work well here. Try the same amount of Stilton instead of the gorgonzola, for a **POINTS** value of 5½ per serving.*

oven baked mushroom and cherry tomato risotto

Baking a risotto means that you don't need to bother continually adding stock and stirring – just pop it in the oven and relax.

Ⓥ *Serves* **4** • *Takes* **10** *minutes to prepare + soaking,* **40** *minutes to cook* • **21½** *POINTS values per recipe* • **380** *calories per serving*

25 g pack dried porcini mushrooms
50 ml (2 fl oz) boiling water
low fat cooking spray
285 g (10 oz) mixed mushrooms, e.g. button and
    chestnut, chopped
2 garlic cloves, chopped
1 sprig of fresh rosemary, needles only
350 g (12 oz) risotto rice
12 cherry tomatoes
75 ml (3 fl oz) Marsala wine
1.2 litres (2 pints) hot vegetable stock
20 g (¾ oz) Parmesan cheese shavings, to serve
salt and freshly ground black pepper

❶ Preheat the oven to Gas Mark 4/180°C/fan oven 160°C. Reconstitute the porcini mushrooms by placing them in a small bowl and covering them with the boiling water. Leave to soak for 10 minutes then drain, reserving the soaking liquid and chop.

❷ Meanwhile, spray a medium, non stick frying pan with the cooking spray and heat until hot. Add all the mushrooms and stir fry for 5 minutes until all the juices released have evaporated. Add the garlic, rosemary and rice and cook for a minute. Remove from the heat and stir in the tomatoes, Marsala, stock and reserved soaking liquid. Spoon into a lidded ovenproof dish, cover and bake for 20 minutes. Remove from the oven, stir well, cover again and bake for a further 15–20 minutes until tender and creamy. Season.

❸ Serve the risotto garnished with the Parmesan shavings.

cheese and bacon gnocchi bake

Serves **2** • *Takes* **25** *minutes to prepare,* **40** *minutes to cook* • **11½** *POINTS values per recipe* • **330** *calories per serving*

175 g (6 oz) floury potatoes such as Désirée,
    peeled and chopped
40 g (1½ oz) self raising flour, plus 1 tablespoon
1 teaspoon dried thyme
1 garlic clove, crushed
For the sauce
15 g (½ oz) low fat polyunsaturated margarine
15 g (½ oz) flour
1 teaspoon mustard powder
300 ml (10 fl oz) skimmed milk
50 g (1¾ oz) reduced fat Cheddar cheese, grated
a handful of young spinach leaves
2 rashers Weight Watchers unsmoked back
    bacon, chopped into pieces

❶ Bring a large, lidded pan of water to the boil. Add the potatoes, cover and simmer for 10–15 minutes until tender. Drain and mash. Stir in the flour, thyme and garlic. Set aside.

❷ Bring another pan of water to the boil. Dust a work surface with 1 tablespoon of flour and shape the potato into long, thin sausages, about 2.5 cm (1 inch) in diameter. Cut off 2.5 cm (1 inch) lengths. Resting the gnocchi on your finger, press the prongs of a fork down on to one side. Add the gnocchi to the pan and cook in batches for 2–3 minutes until they rise to the surface. Use a slotted spoon to remove to an ovenproof dish.

❸ Preheat the oven to Gas Mark 5/190°C/fan oven 170°C. Melt the margarine in a small pan. Stir in the flour and mustard powder. Cook gently for a minute then remove from the heat. Add the milk a bit at a time, beating the mixture to a smooth sauce each time. Add the spinach and half the cheese.

❹ Spoon the sauce over the gnocchi. Sprinkle over the remaining cheese. Scatter over the bacon. Place on a baking tray and bake for 20 minutes.

artichoke and green olive pizza

Get the kids to help make this pizza – they will enjoy kneading the dough and eating their own handiwork.

Ⓨ *Serves* **2** • *Takes* **15** *minutes to prepare + rising,* **10** *minutes to cook* • **12** *POINTS values per recipe* • **387** *calories per serving*

175 g (6 oz) strong white flour, plus 1 tablespoon
    for dusting
½ teaspoon fast action dried yeast
½ teaspoon sugar
½ teaspoon salt
1 teaspoon mixed dried herbs
2 vine ripened tomatoes, sliced
3 artichoke hearts in brine from a can or jar,
    drained and quartered
25 g (1 oz) pitted green olives in brine, drained
    and halved
40 g (1½ oz) Weight Watchers Cheddar cheese,
    grated
a handful of fresh basil leaves, to garnish
salt and freshly ground black pepper

❶ To make the base, place the flour, yeast, sugar and salt in a bowl with the herbs and mix together. Add 125 ml (4 fl oz) hand hot water and mix to a dough. Use half of the reserved flour to dust a work surface and knead the dough for 5 minutes until smooth and elastic. Return to the bowl and leave in a warm place for about 20 minutes until doubled in size.

❷ Preheat the oven to Gas Mark 6/200°C/fan oven 180°C. Knock back the dough by punching it down. Use the remaining flour to dust a work surface and then knead for a minute or so. Divide the dough in two and roll each to a round approximately 15 cm (6 inches) in diameter. Place on a non stick baking tray. Top with the sliced tomatoes, then the artichokes, olives and finally the cheese. Season and bake for 10–15 minutes until the base is golden and risen. Garnish with fresh basil before serving.

giant shells with spinach and basil pesto

When you make your own pesto, not only do you get a wonderful fresh basil flavour but you can keep it low in POINTS values.

Ⓨ *Serves* **2** • *Takes* **25** *minutes* • **12½** *POINTS values per recipe* • **409** *calories per serving*

15 g (½ oz) Parmesan cheese
15 g (½ oz) pine nut kernels
25 g bag basil leaves, a few reserved for
    garnish
1 small garlic clove, peeled
2 teaspoons extra virgin olive oil
To serve
150 g (5½ oz) giant pasta shells
low fat cooking spray
4 spring onions, chopped
75 g (2¾ oz) spinach

❶ For the pesto, place the Parmesan and pine nut kernels in a blender or food processor and whizz to crumbs. Add the basil and garlic and whizz again. Then add the oil and blend to a thick paste. Set aside.

❷ Bring a large pan of water to the boil, add the pasta shells, bring back to the boil and cook according to the packet instructions. Drain well, reserving 4 tablespoons of the cooking liquid. Return the pasta to the pan.

❸ Meanwhile, spray a medium, non stick frying pan with the cooking spray and heat until hot. Add the spring onions and stir fry for 2 minutes until softened. Add the spinach and cook for a further minute until just wilted. Remove from the heat.

❹ Stir the spinach mixture into the pasta with the pesto and reserved cooking liquid. Gently warm through, stirring continuously until hot. Serve garnished with reserved basil leaves.

Tip *The pesto will keep in the fridge, covered, for 5 days.*

pizza bianco

Most pizzas start with a tomato base which adds flavour and keeps the pizza moist. Pizza bianco however is white and has no tomatoes – instead it is covered with deliciously sweet, caramelised onions.

Serves **2** • *Takes* **10** *minutes to prepare,* **40** *minutes to cook* • **12½** *POINTS values per recipe* • **433** *calories per serving*

1 tablespoon olive oil

3 onions, sliced thinly

2 sprigs of fresh rosemary

2 garlic cloves, sliced thinly

1 tablespoon capers in brine, rinsed

150 g ready made thin and crispy pizza base (see tip)

4 anchovies in oil (20 g total weight), drained, rinsed and halved lengthways

60 g (2 oz) ricotta cheese

salt and freshly ground black pepper

❶ Heat the oil in a lidded saucepan until hot. Add the onions and stir fry for 5 minutes until beginning to soften. Add the rosemary and garlic and stir well. Reduce the heat to low then cover the onions with a layer of greaseproof paper that actually touches them. Cover with a lid and leave to cook undisturbed for 30 minutes. Remove from the heat, take out the stems of rosemary (most of the needles should have fallen off), stir in the capers and season to taste.

❷ Preheat the oven to Gas Mark 7/220°C/fan oven 200°C and place a baking tray in the oven to heat up. Spread the onion mix over the pizza base, top with the anchovies and dollop teaspoons of ricotta on top so that they nestle in the onions. Place on the pre-heated baking tray and bake for 10 minutes until the base is golden. Serve warm.

Tip *Ready made pizza bases are usually available in packs of two. You can freeze the remaining uncooked, ready made pizza and use it another time.*

chicken and thyme risotto

Serves **2** • *Takes* **45** *minutes* • **13** *POINTS values per recipe* • **470** *calories per serving*

low fat cooking spray

2 x 150 g (5½ oz) skinless boneless chicken breasts, cut into thin strips

1 red onion, sliced

2 garlic cloves, sliced

2 sprigs of fresh thyme, plus extra to garnish

150 g (5½ oz) risotto rice

50 ml (2 fl oz) red wine

600 ml (1 pint) hot chicken stock

salt and freshly ground black pepper

❶ Spray a large, non stick frying pan with the cooking spray and heat until hot. Add the chicken strips and stir fry for 3–4 minutes until brown and cooked through. Remove from the pan and set aside on a plate.

❷ Spray the pan again with the cooking spray and heat until hot. Add the onion and cook, stirring for 3 minutes. Add 1 tablespoon of water, the garlic and thyme and cook for 2 minutes. Add the rice and cook for a further minute.

❸ Stir in the wine. It will bubble up rapidly and virtually evaporate. Add a ladleful of stock, reduce the heat and let it be absorbed before adding more, a little at a time. Stir occasionally until all the stock has been used and the rice is tender.

❹ Return the chicken to the pan and heat through gently. Season and garnish with thyme.

Variations *You can try this with four rashers of lean back bacon, pan fried in strips in step 1 instead of the chicken, for a POINTS value of 7 per serving.*

Ⓥ *For a vegetarian version, omit the chicken, change the stock to vegetable and stir in a 150 g pack of marinated tofu pieces in step 4, heating through until hot, for 5 POINTS values per serving.*

chicken calzone

Serves **4** • Takes **25** minutes to prepare + rising,
10–15 minutes to cook • **26½ POINTS** values per
recipe • **336** calories per serving

245 g pack pizza dough mix
2 teaspoons dried oregano
low fat cooking spray
200 g (7 oz) skinless boneless chicken breasts,
    diced
1 small red onion, **chopped**
125 g pack soft mozzarella light, chopped
3 tomatoes, **chopped roughly**
a handful of basil **leaves**
1 egg white, **beaten lightly**
1 tablespoon flour, for dusting
zero POINTS value green salad, **to serve**
salt and freshly ground black pepper

❶ Make up the pizza dough according to the
packet instructions, stirring in the oregano before
adding the water. Cover and leave in a warm place
until doubled in size, while you make the filling.
❷ Spray a non stick frying pan with the cooking
spray and heat until hot. Add the chicken pieces and
onion and stir fry for 5–7 minutes until brown and
cooked through. Set aside to cool a little.
❸ Preheat the oven to Gas Mark 7/220°C/fan oven
200°C. Dust a work surface with ½ a tablespoon
of flour. Divide the dough into four and roll each
into a circle approximately 15 cm (6 inches) in
diameter. Top one half of the circle with a quarter of
the chicken mixture, and a quarter of the cheese,
tomatoes and basil each. Season and brush around
the edge with the egg white. Fold over the dough
to create a semi circle and squeeze together the
edges to seal. Repeat to make four in total.
❹ Dust a baking tray with the remaining flour,
transfer all the calzone and brush the tops with the
remaining egg white. Bake for 10–15 minutes until
golden and puffed up. Serve warm with the salad.

creamy beef and mushroom pasta

This is a really quick supper dish and it's delicious
with a zero **POINTS** value green salad.

Serves **2** • Takes **15–20** minutes • **14 POINTS** values
per recipe • **445** calories per serving

200 g (7 oz) fresh tagliatelle
175 g (6 oz) rump steak, **fat removed**
low fat cooking spray
110 g (4 oz) chestnut mushrooms, **sliced**
2 garlic cloves, **sliced**
100 ml (3½ fl oz) hot beef stock
60 g (2 oz) low fat soft cheese
1 tablespoon chopped fresh tarragon, **plus extra**
    to garnish
salt and freshly ground black pepper

❶ Season the steak on both sides. Heat a medium
non stick frying pan until hot. Add the steak and fry
for 2–4 minutes on each side, depending on how
well done you like it. Remove from the pan, cover
with foil and leave to rest.
❷ Spray the pan with the cooking spray and add
the mushrooms. Cook for 5 minutes until the juices
released have evaporated. Add the garlic and cook
for a further 1 minute. Add the stock, bring to the
boil and simmer for 2 minutes before stirring in the
soft cheese. Reduce the heat and warm through,
stirring in the tarragon and season.
❸ Meanwhile, bring a large pan of water to the
boil, add the pasta and cook according to the packet
instructions. Drain well.
❹ Slice the steak into thin strips and add to the
sauce. Refresh and warm the pasta by running very
hot water over it in the colander. Serve the pasta
in bowls with the steak and sauce on top. Garnish
with a little tarragon.

Ⓨ **Variation** For a vegetarian version, change the
stock to vegetable, omit the steak and stir in 110 g
(4 oz) Quorn Deli Style Ham, cut into strips, with
the stock. The **POINTS** values per serving will be 6.

warm roasted prawn salad

1 POINTS VALUE

*Serves **4** • Takes **15** minutes to prepare, **35** minutes to cook • **4½ POINTS** values per recipe • **151** calories per serving*

1 aubergine**, trimmed and cut into chunks**
2 red onions**, peeled and cut into wedges**
300 g (10½ oz) butternut squash**, peeled and cut into chunks**
8 garlic cloves**, whole**
1 lemon**, cut into wedges**
2 sprigs of fresh rosemary
low fat cooking spray
2 teaspoons fennel seeds
400 g (14 oz) raw king prawns**, tail on**
60 g (2 oz) spinach leaves
60 g (2 oz) rocket leaves
2 tablespoons balsamic vinegar
salt and freshly ground black pepper

❶ Preheat the oven to Gas Mark 6/200°C/fan oven 180°C. Place the aubergine, onions and squash in a large roasting tin with the garlic, lemon and rosemary. Season, spray with the cooking spray, scatter over the fennel seeds and roast for 25 minutes. Remove from the oven, stir the vegetables and place the prawns on top. Return to the oven for 10 minutes until the prawns are cooked through and the vegetables lightly charred. Remove and cool slightly.

❷ Divide the spinach and rocket leaves between four serving plates and top with the roasted vegetables and prawns. Drizzle over the balsamic vinegar just before serving.

Tip To use ready cooked prawns, spray the pan with cooking spray and fry over a medium heat for 1–2 minutes until hot, or add them cold to your salad.

Goes well with...

*The Strawberry and Chocolate Tiramisu on page 59 for a lovely alfresco lunch and an extra 4 **POINTS** values per serving.*

Fish and seafood are an ideal choice for a main meal. All the recipes are low in **POINTS** values and rich in taste so you're sure to be inspired.

fish cakes

*Home made fish cakes are a great way to get the family to enjoy fish. Serve with a zero **POINTS** value green salad.*

*Serves **4** • Takes **15** minutes to prepare, **40–45** minutes to cook • **8½ POINTS** values per recipe • **164** calories per serving*

225 g (8 oz) skinless haddock
350 g (12 oz) potatoes, **peeled and cut in chunks**
2 tablespoons (30 g/1¼ oz total weight) reduced fat pesto
4 spring onions, **chopped**
25 g (1 oz) natural dried breadcrumbs
low fat cooking spray
4 tablespoons 0% fat Greek yogurt
finely grated zest of ½ a lemon
1 tablespoon chopped fresh parsley

❶ Place the fish in a shallow, lidded pan and cover with water. Bring to the boil, cover and simmer gently for 5 minutes. Drain well and flake the fish into chunks. Set aside to cool.
❷ Bring a large pan of water to the boil, add the potatoes and cook for 10–15 minutes until tender. Drain and mash.
❸ Stir the fish flakes into the mashed potatoes with the pesto and spring onions. Set aside until cool enough to handle.
❹ Preheat the oven to Gas Mark 6/200°C/fan oven 180°C. Line a baking tray with non stick baking parchment. Shape the fish mixture into eight fish cakes. Place the breadcrumbs in a shallow bowl. Coat each fish cake in the breadcrumbs, making sure they are evenly covered before placing on the baking tray. Spray each with the cooking spray and bake for 30 minutes until golden.
❺ Mix together the yogurt, lemon zest and parsley and serve on the side with the fish cakes.

*Variation You can make the fish cakes with the same amount of **salmon**, in place of the haddock, for a **POINTS** value of 3½ per serving.*

seafood lasagne

*Serves **6** • Takes **15** minutes to prepare, **40–50** minutes to cook • **22½ POINTS** values per recipe • **215** calories per serving*

low fat cooking spray
2 leeks, **sliced finely**
2 x 250 g punnets mixed seafood **eg squid, mussels, prawns**
50 ml (2 fl oz) white wine
1 fish or vegetable stock cube, crumbled
15 g (½ oz) low fat polyunsaturated margarine
15 g (½ oz) flour
600 ml (1 pint) skimmed milk
25 g pack dill, **chopped**
150 g (5½ oz) ready to cook lasagne **sheets**
1 egg, **beaten**
8 cherry tomatoes, **halved**
25 g (1 oz) mature Cheddar cheese, grated
salt and freshly ground black pepper

❶ Preheat the oven to Gas Mark 5/190°C/fan oven 170°C. Spray a large, non stick frying pan with the cooking spray and heat until hot. Add the leeks and stir fry for 5 minutes until softened. Add the seafood, wine and stock cube and heat through for a few minutes. Remove from the heat.
❷ To make the sauce, melt the margarine in a small pan then stir in the flour. Cook for 1 minute then remove from the heat. Add the milk a little at a time, stirring to a smooth paste each time before adding more. Stir in the dill and season.
❸ Pour half the sauce (reserving the other half) into the seafood mixture and stir well. Spoon half of this mixture into an 25 cm (10 inch) square ovenproof dish. Top with half of the lasagne sheets, the remaining seafood mixture and the rest of the lasagne sheets.
❹ Beat the egg into the reserved sauce and spread over the top of the lasagne. Scatter over the tomatoes and sprinkle over the cheese. Place on a baking tray and bake for 40–50 minutes until cooked through and golden on top.

braised sea bass with fresh tomato sauce

Serves **4** • Takes **10** minutes to prepare, **25** minutes to cook • **16 POINTS** values per recipe • **300** calories per serving

450 g (1 lb) new potatoes
low fat cooking spray
1 onion**, chopped**
2 garlic cloves**, crushed**
450 g (1 lb) vine ripened tomatoes**, chopped**
1 tablespoon tomato purée
½ vegetable stock cube
50 ml (2 fl oz) white wine
60 g (2 oz) black olives in brine**, drained and sliced**
a handful of basil **leaves, plus extra to garnish**
8 x 75 g (2¾ oz) sea bass **fillets**
salt and freshly ground black pepper

❶ Preheat the oven to Gas Mark 5/190°C/fan oven 170°C. Bring a saucepan of water to the boil, add the potatoes and cook for 15 minutes or until tender. Drain.

❷ Meanwhile, spray a medium, lidded saucepan with the cooking spray and heat until hot. Add the onion and cook, stirring, for 3 minutes until beginning to soften. Add the garlic and cook for a further minute. Add the tomatoes, tomato purée, stock cube and the wine and 50 ml (2 fl oz) water. Bring to the boil, cover, reduce the heat and simmer for 10 minutes until soft. Stir in the olives and basil.

❸ Spoon the sauce into an ovenproof dish. Season the fish on both sides and lay on top of the sauce. Bake for 10 minutes until the fish just flakes.

❹ Serve the fish with the sauce spooned over, scattered with the remaining basil leaves and the potatoes on the side.

Variation Try this recipe with the same amount of **mackerel** fillets, in place of the seabass and the **POINTS** values will be 7½ per serving.

Florentine toast

This makes a lovely brunch dish.

Serves **1** • Takes **15** minutes • **4 POINTS** values per recipe • **285** calories per serving

125 g (4½ oz) skinless smoked haddock fillet
1 bay leaf
1 egg
low fat cooking spray
4 cherry tomatoes
a large handful of spinach
1 garlic clove**, sliced**
1 medium slice wholemeal bread
freshly ground black pepper

❶ Place the haddock and bay leaf in a small lidded, shallow pan and cover with water. Bring to the boil, cover and simmer gently for 5 minutes until the fish just flakes. Using a slotted spoon, remove the fish to a plate, cover and keep warm. Discard the bay leaf.

❷ Bring the water which the haddock was in back to the boil and reduce to simmer. Crack the egg into a small cup, stir the water creating a whirlpool effect and carefully add the egg to the water. Cook for 3 minutes until the white is just set. Remove with a slotted spoon.

❸ Meanwhile, spray a small, non stick frying pan with the cooking spray and heat until hot. Add the tomatoes and fry for 2 minutes. Add the spinach and garlic with a tablespoon of water and continue cooking until the spinach has wilted. Remove from the heat.

❹ Toast the bread until golden, then top with the spinach and tomatoes, haddock and poached egg. Season with black pepper and serve.

Tip The bay leaf reduces the odour of the fish whilst cooking.

herb crusted salmon

This is a quick and easy supper dish. It's delicious with steamed green beans and broccoli, for no extra POINTS values.

Serves 4 • Takes 10 minutes to prepare, 15–20 minutes to cook • 20 POINTS values per recipe • 304 calories per serving

40 g (1½ oz) ciabatta bread
2 teaspoons dried oregano
1 tablespoon fresh rosemary needles
finely grated zest and juice of 1 lemon, plus
    lemon wedges to serve
1 tablespoon freshly grated Parmesan cheese
low fat cooking spray
4 x 150 g (5½ oz) pieces salmon fillet, skinned

❶ Preheat the oven to Gas Mark 6/200°C/fan oven 180°C. Break the bread into pieces and place in a food processor or blender. Whizz to fine breadcrumbs, then add the oregano, rosemary, lemon zest and Parmesan. Blend briefly to combine.

❷ Line a baking tray with foil and spray with the cooking spray. Place the salmon fillets on the tray and divide the topping between them, coating the top. Drizzle over the lemon juice and spray with the cooking spray. Bake for 15–20 minutes until golden and the fish is cooked.

Tip *You can make extra topping and freeze it for the next time.*

roast trout with almond stuffing

Two fillets of trout sandwiched together with an almond stuffing and then baked in the oven make a great supper party dish. Serve with steamed green beans and 60 g (2 oz) dried brown rice per person, cooked according to the packet instructions, for an extra 3 POINTS values per serving.

Serves 4 • Takes 20 minutes to prepare, 20 minutes to cook • 22 POINTS values per recipe • 423 calories per serving

low fat cooking spray

1 onion, diced

150 g (5½ oz) mushrooms, chopped finely

110 g (4 oz) ground almonds

3 anchovies in oil from a jar (15 g in total), drained, rinsed and chopped

2 tablespoons capers in brine, rinsed and chopped

finely grated zest and juice of 1 lime, plus wedges

8 x 90 g (3¼ oz) trout fillets

salt and freshly ground black pepper

① Preheat the oven to Gas Mark 6/200°C/fan oven 180°C. Spray a non stick frying pan with the cooking spray and heat until hot. Add the onion and mushrooms and cook for 5–7 minutes until soft. Remove from the heat and stir in the ground almonds, anchovies, capers and lime zest.

② Season the fillets on both sides. Line a shallow roasting tin with foil and spray with the cooking spray. Place four fillets skin side down on the tin. Divide the stuffing between the fillets, spread out evenly and squeeze over the lime juice. Top with the other fillets and, to secure, tie together with string in at least two places, to secure. Bake for 20 minutes and serve with the lime wedges.

Goes well with...

The Olive Dip with Melba Toast on page 8 as a starter for a supper party and an extra 1½ POINTS values per serving.

smoked mackerel pasta

This pasta dish is packed with robust flavours which go surprisingly well together.

Serves 2 • Takes 20 minutes • 16 POINTS values per recipe • 456 calories per serving

110 g (4 oz) wholemeal pasta shapes, e.g. penne

50 g (1¾ oz) broccoli florets

110 g (4 oz) smoked mackerel fillets, skinned and flaked

3 small vine ripened tomatoes, quartered

For the pesto sauce

25 g (1 oz) basil leaves

1 tablespoon pine nut kernels

1 tablespoon finely grated Parmesan cheese

1 garlic clove, peeled

① Bring a large pan of water to the boil, add the pasta and cook according to the packet instructions. Add the broccoli for the final 4 minutes of cooking time. Drain well and return to the pan.

② Toast the pine nut kernels by dry-frying them in a frying pan for a couple of minutes until they begin to brown. Skin and flake the mackerel and add to the pan with the tomatoes.

③ To make the pesto, place all the ingredients in a small blender and whizz to a paste. Add 2 tablespoons of warm water and blend again.

④ Pour the pesto sauce into the pasta mixture, stir well and heat through over a low heat until piping hot.

Variation *If you prefer, you can use 2 tablespoons of ready made reduced fat pesto, instead of the home made pesto, for a POINTS value of 7 per serving.*

Parma wrapped pork fillet

Pork fillet or tenderloin is a lovely lean cut which lends itself to being wrapped and pan fried, as it is here with Parma ham. Serve with steamed green vegetables, such as green beans, for no additional POINTS values.

Serves 4 • Takes 15 minutes to prepare, 20 minutes to cook • 11 POINTS values per recipe • 182 calories per serving

4 x 12 g slices Parma ham
400 g (14 oz) piece of pork tenderloin
low fat cooking spray
2 red onions**, sliced**
50 ml (2 fl oz) Marsala wine
200 ml (7 fl oz) chicken stock
salt and freshly ground black pepper

❶ If your tenderloin is too big for the frying pan, cut it into two pieces. Lay the slices of Parma ham on a board and put the pork tenderloin on top. Season and wrap the ham around the pork.

❷ Spray a lidded, non stick frying pan (if you don't have a lid, you can cover it with a baking tray) with the cooking spray and heat until hot. Add the pork and cook over a high heat for 2–3 minutes, turning until golden all over. Remove to a plate.

❸ Add the onions and stir fry for 3 minutes then return the pork to the pan with the Marsala and stock. Bring to the boil, cover and simmer for 20 minutes. The pork should be cooked through in the middle. Slice it in half and if it is still pink, return it to the pan for a few minutes.

❹ To serve, slice the pork and arrange on plates with the onions and sauce.

Tip *If you don't have any Marsala wine, use the same amount of medium sherry or Port instead, for the same POINTS values per serving.*

Here you'll find old favourites as well as new ideas for pork, beef, lamb and poultry to bring a taste of Italy into your kitchen.

saltimbocca

Traditionally made with veal, this version uses turkey fillets which are flattened and rolled up with sage before being pan fried and braised in stock.

*Serves **2** • Takes **30** minutes • **6 POINTS** values per recipe • **191** calories per serving*

2 x 125 g (4½ oz) turkey fillets
6 sage leaves, plus extra to garnish
4 x 10 g (¼ oz) slices prosciutto
6 shallots, halved if large
300 ml (10 fl oz) hot chicken stock
salt and freshly ground black pepper

❶ Cover a chopping board with clingfilm and place the turkey on top. Cover with another sheet of clingfilm then bash with the end of a rolling pin, or a small frying pan, until about 5 cm (2 inches) thick. Discard the clingfilm and season each fillet. Place 3 sage leaves and 2 slices of prosciutto on each fillet and roll up. If needs be, secure with a wooden cocktail stick.

❷ Heat a lidded, non stick frying pan until hot. Add the turkey roll ups, placing them seam side down and brown slightly to lock in the flavour. Once sealed, add the shallots and turn the rolls so that they brown all over. Add the stock and bring to the boil. Cover and reduce to a simmer for 10 minutes until cooked through. Remove the turkey to a plate, covering it with foil to keep it warm. Increase the heat and boil the sauce for 2 to 3 minutes until slightly reduced and thickened. Serve the turkey with the sauce, garnished with the extra sage leaves.

Serving suggestion *Serve with 60 g (2 oz) dried brown rice per person, cooked according to the packet instructions. Stir in 75 g (2¾ oz) spinach so that it just wilts. This will add 3 **POINTS** values per serving.*

marinated chicken salad

*Serves **4** • Takes **10** minutes to prepare + marinating, **40** minutes to cook • **13½ POINTS** values per recipe • **273** calories per serving*

4 x 125 g (4½ oz) skinless boneless chicken breasts
1 tablespoon chopped fresh rosemary
finely grated zest and juice of 2 limes, plus wedges to serve
2 garlic cloves, sliced
1 red chilli, de-seeded and diced
1 large courgette, cut into chunks
450 g (1 lb) sweet potato, peeled and cut into chunks
2 red peppers, de-seeded and cut into chunks
low fat cooking spray
salt and freshly ground black pepper
To serve
mixed salad leaves
fat free vinaigrette

❶ Place the chicken breasts, rosemary, lime zest and juice, garlic and chilli in a large non metallic bowl. Stir well to coat the meat. Cover and leave to marinate at room temperature for 20 minutes.

❷ Meanwhile, preheat the oven to Gas Mark 6/200°C/fan oven 180°C. Place the vegetables in a large roasting tin, spray with the cooking spray and roast for 20 minutes. Remove from the oven, add the chicken breasts and any marinade on top of the vegetables and season. Spray again with the cooking spray. Roast for a further 20 minutes until the chicken is cooked – a skewer inserted into the thickest part of the chicken should make the juices run clear.

❸ Slice the chicken breast and serve on top of a quarter of the vegetables with some salad leaves and vinaigrette drizzled over.

Ⓥ **Variation** *For a vegetarian version, replace the chicken with 60 g (2 oz) sliced light halloumi per person, for a **POINTS** value of 2 per serving.*

braised pork chops

This is a quick and easy all in one dish - great for a midweek meal.

Serves **4** • Takes **10** minutes to prepare, **40** minutes to cook • **15 POINTS** values per recipe • **521** calories per serving

700 g (1 lb 9 oz) plum tomatoes, halved
3 garlic cloves, sliced
2 fennel bulbs, trimmed and sliced
2 yellow peppers, de-seeded and cut into thin strips
finely grated zest and juice of 1 lemon
4 x 175 g (6 oz) pork chops
150 ml (5 fl oz) chicken stock
a handful of basil leaves, to garnish
salt and freshly ground black pepper

❶ Preheat the oven to Gas Mark 5/190°C/fan oven 170°C. In a large, lidded, ovenproof dish, mix together the tomatoes, garlic, fennel, peppers and lemon zest. Place the pork chops on top and pour over the stock. Season well. Drizzle with the lemon juice. Cover and bake for 30 minutes.

❷ Remove the lid and bake for a further 10 minutes until the pork is golden and cooked through and all the vegetables have softened.

❸ Garnish with the basil leaves before serving.

Variation This works well with four 125 g (4½ oz) skinless boneless chicken breasts, instead of the pork, for a **POINTS** value of 2 per serving.

Serving suggestion Serve with 60 g (2 oz) fresh tagliatelle per person, cooked according to the packet instructions and tossed with 1 tablespoon of chopped parsley, for an extra 2½ **POINTS** values per serving.

leg of lamb with roasted onions and cannellini beans

Serves **6** • Takes **15** minutes to prepare + marinating + resting, **1 hour 10** minutes to cook • **27 POINTS** values per recipe • **329** calories per serving

1.25 kg (2 lb 12 oz) leg of lamb
3 garlic cloves, sliced
300 ml (10 fl oz) red wine
2 sprigs of fresh rosemary, leaves removed and chopped roughly
finely grated zest and juice of a lemon
6 onions, halved
2 x 400 g cans cannellini beans, drained
400 g can tomatoes with herbs and garlic
6 (30 g/1¼ oz) sun-dried tomatoes, reconstituted according to the packet instructions
salt and freshly ground black pepper

❶ Make lots of small incisions in the lamb and stuff with slices of garlic. In a jug, mix together the red wine, rosemary, lemon zest and juice. Place the lamb in a non metallic bowl and pour over the marinade. Cover and refrigerate for at least 6 hours or overnight if possible.

❷ Preheat the oven to Gas Mark 7/220°C/fan oven 200°C. Drain the lamb, reserving the marinade. Place the lamb in a large roasting tin, season and cook for 20 minutes before reducing the temperature to Gas Mark 5/190°C/fan oven 170°C. Add the onions and continue cooking for about 50 minutes. Remove from the oven, cover with foil and leave for at least 20 minutes before carving.

❸ Meanwhile, place the beans and tomatoes in a small pan over a gentle heat. Drain the sun-dried tomatoes. Cut into small pieces and add to the pan. Add half the reserved marinade from the lamb, discard the rest and simmer gently for 10 minutes until slightly thickened. Season.

❹ Slice the lamb, allowing 75 g (2¾ oz) per person. Serve with the onions and the bean mixture.

4 1/2
POINTS
VALUE

rosemary pork skewers with fresh pepper sauce

Using rosemary sticks for skewers helps to infuse the meat with the full flavour of the herb and they look impressive too.

Serves **4** • *Takes* **35** *minutes to prepare,* **10–15** *minutes to cook* • **20 POINTS** *values per recipe* • **343** *calories per serving*

3 red peppers, **halved and de-seeded**
175 g (6 oz) brown rice
110 g (4 oz) green beans, **chopped into 10 cm (4 inches) pieces**
8 sprigs of fresh rosemary, **about 20 cm (8 inches) long**
400 g (14 oz) pork loin, **cubed**
1 courgette, **cut into rounds and then halved**
low fat cooking spray
1 tablespoon olive oil
2 teaspoons white wine vinegar
salt and freshly ground black pepper

❶ Preheat the grill to medium hot. Place the peppers skin side up under the grill for 3–4 minutes until black. Place the charred peppers in a plastic bag and set aside until step 4. This helps to loosen the skin.

❷ Meanwhile, bring a large pan of water to the boil, add the rice, bring back to the boil and cook according to the packet instructions. Add the beans for the final 4 minutes of cooking time. Drain and cover to keep warm.

❸ Turn down the grill to medium. Remove some of the needles from the rosemary sprigs, reserving a tablespoon, and set aside. Thread the pork cubes and courgette pieces on to the eight rosemary skewers (it's easier if you pierce a hole in the pork with a metal skewer before threading it on to the rosemary). Spray with the cooking spray and grill, turning regularly for 10–15 minutes, until cooked through.

❹ Take the peppers from the bag. Remove the skin and discard. Roughly chop the peppers, place in a liquidiser or blender, and blend to a paste. Add the oil and vinegar with a little seasoning and the reserved rosemary needles and blend again.

❺ Serve two skewers each with the rice and beans and the sauce on the side.

Ⓥ **Variation** *For a vegetarian option, thread two 150 g packs of marinated tofu pieces on to the rosemary skewers instead of pork, for a* **POINTS** *value of 3½ per serving.*

lamb chops with Italian potatoes

Serves **4** • Takes **10** minutes to prepare, **10–15** minutes to cook • **20 POINTS** values per recipe
• **268** calories per serving

8 x 75 g (2¾ oz) lamb chops, fat removed
low fat cooking spray
450 g (1 lb) new potatoes, scrubbed and diced
12 cherry tomatoes, halved
75 g (2¾ oz) pitted black olives in brine, drained
    and halved
110 g (4 oz) spinach
salt and freshly ground black pepper

❶ Preheat the grill to medium. Season the chops on both sides then grill for 10–12 minutes, turning once until just cooked through.

❷ Meanwhile, spray a large, non stick frying pan with the cooking spray and heat until hot. Add the potatoes and stir fry for 10–15 minutes until tender, adding a little water if they begin to stick.

❸ Add the tomatoes and olives. Cook for a minute before adding the spinach. Toss the mixture for a minute or so, until the spinach just starts to wilt. Season. Serve the lamb chops on top of the potatoes.

Variation *You can replace the lamb with a 250 g pack of Quorn sausages, grilled according to the packet instructions, for a **POINTS** value of 2½ per serving.*

steak with caponata

Serves **2** • Takes **45** minutes • **10 POINTS** values per recipe • **386** calories per serving

1 large aubergine
low fat cooking spray
1 red onion, sliced
1 celery stick, chopped
2 garlic cloves, crushed
400 g can chopped tomatoes
40 g (1½ oz) pitted green olives in brine,
    chopped
2 tablespoons capers in brine, rinsed
40 g (1½ oz) raisins
2 tablespoons red wine vinegar
1 teaspoon sugar
2 x 150 g (5½ oz) sirloin steak
a handful of chopped fresh parsley, to garnish

❶ Preheat a griddle pan or non stick frying pan until hot. Slice the aubergine along its length and spray each piece with the cooking spray. Griddle the pieces, turning once until softened. You will need to do this batches. Once cooked, cut the aubergine into bite size pieces.

❷ Spray a medium sized, lidded pan with the cooking spray and heat until hot. Add the onion and celery and stir fry for 10 minutes until softened. Add the garlic, tomatoes and aubergines, then stir in the olives, capers, raisins, vinegar and sugar. Slowly bring to the boil, cover and simmer for 10 minutes.

❸ Meanwhile, spray the same pan used in step one with the cooking spray. Heat until hot. Add the steak. Cook for 4–5 minutes, turning once for medium, slightly less for rare and more for well done. Serve the steak on top of the caponata, garnished with parsley.

Goes well with...

*The Zabaglione with Raspberries (half the recipe) on page 59 for a special meal for two and an extra 3 **POINTS** values per serving.*

whole roasted chicken with garlic and lemon

Serves **4** • Takes **20** minutes to prepare, **1 hour 20** minutes to cook • **19½ POINTS** values per recipe • **367** calories per serving

1.5 kg (3 lb 5 oz) chicken, giblets removed
2 lemons, 1 sliced, 1 quartered
2 garlic cloves, sliced
2 sprigs of fresh rosemary
450 g (1 lb) new potatoes, halved if large
4 sprigs of fresh thyme
low fat cooking spray
salt and freshly ground black pepper
To serve
150 g bag watercress and rocket leaves
4 large vine ripened tomatoes, sliced
4 tablespoons balsamic vinegar

❶ Preheat the oven to Gas Mark 6/200°C/fan oven 180°C. Gently loosen the skin of the chicken by working your fingers carefully under the skin, separating the skin and meat and moving up over the breast. Slide under as many lemon and garlic slices as you can. Smooth the skin back into place. Push the lemon quarters inside the chicken cavity with the rosemary. Season. Place in a roasting tin and roast for 20 minutes. Reduce the heat to Gas Mark 4/180°C/fan oven 160°C and continue cooking for an hour. Test that the chicken is cooked by inserting a skewer into the thickest part and seeing that the juices run clear.

❷ Meanwhile, place the potatoes in a small roasting tin, scatter over the thyme and season. Spray with the cooking spray and roast for 40 minutes, turning occasionally.

❸ To serve, allow 75 g (2¾ oz) skinless breast and 75 g (2¾ oz) skinless leg meat per person with a quarter of the potatoes. Discard the lemon slices but retain the garlic to serve. Drizzle the watercress, rocket and tomatoes with the vinegar.

chicken with olives and oregano

This Italian style chicken casserole is a great make ahead supper. Serve with 125 g (4½ oz) potato, mashed with 1 tablespoon of skimmed milk per person, for an extra 1½ **POINTS** values per serving.

✳ Serves **4** • Takes **10** minutes to prepare, **1 hour 10** minutes to cook • **23½ POINTS** values per recipe • **220** calories per serving

low fat cooking spray
400 g (14 oz) skinless chicken drumsticks
400 g (14 oz) skinless chicken thighs
1 red pepper, de-seeded and cut into strips
1 yellow pepper, de-seeded and cut into strips
4 plum tomatoes, halved
50 g (1¾ oz) pitted black olives in brine, drained
2 garlic cloves, sliced
1 bay leaf and 2 sprigs of fresh oregano, tied together
450 ml (16 fl oz) hot chicken stock
2 tablespoons chopped fresh parsley, to garnish
salt and freshly ground black pepper

❶ Preheat the oven to Gas Mark 4/180°C/fan oven 160°C. Spray a large, lidded, ovenproof casserole dish with the cooking spray and heat until hot. Add the drumsticks and thighs and cook until brown. You may need to do this in batches. Remove with a slotted spoon and keep warm. Add the peppers to the dish and cook for 2–3 minutes until softened.

❷ Add all the remaining ingredients, including the chicken, to the pan at the same time. Bring to the boil, cover and cook in the oven for an hour until the chicken is falling from the bone. Season.

❸ Serve the stew garnished with the parsley.

Variation If you prefer, you could use a 400 g can of whole tomatoes, instead of the fresh ones, for the same **POINTS** values.

bolognese stuffed peppers

If you can't find ramiro peppers, ordinary ones will do.

Serves **4** • *Takes* **10** *minutes to prepare,* **55** *minutes to cook* • **25 POINTS** *values per recipe* • **386** *calories per serving*

low fat cooking spray
450 g (1lb) lean minced beef
1 onion, diced
2 garlic cloves, crushed
1 carrot, peeled and diced
400 g can chopped tomatoes
50 ml (2 fl oz) red wine
1 beef stock cube, crumbled
4 ramiro peppers
150 g (5½ oz) brown rice
110 g (4 oz) frozen peas
2 tablespoons chopped fresh parsley

❶ Preheat the oven to Gas Mark 6/200°C/fan oven 180°C. Spray a large saucepan with the cooking spray and heat until hot. Add the beef and cook, stirring until brown. Add the onion and cook for 2 minutes before adding the garlic, carrot, tomatoes, wine and stock cube. Bring to the boil and simmer gently, uncovered, for 20 minutes until the vegetables are tender and the mixture is quite thick.

❷ Slice the peppers in half along their length, removing any seeds. Place on a baking tray and spoon in the bolognese mixture. Cover with foil and cook for 30 minutes, removing the foil for the last 10 minutes of cooking time.

❸ Meanwhile, bring a large pan of water to the boil, add the rice, return to the boil and cook according to the packet instructions. Add the peas for the final 5 minutes of cooking time. Drain well and stir through the parsley. Serve the peppers with the rice on the side.

Tip *The filling for these peppers can be served with pasta or used as the base for a lasagne.*

red wine braised beef

This is a rich beef stew, often made with the famous Italian Barolo wine and is a great make ahead dinner.

❄ *Serves* **4** • *Takes* **30** *minutes to prepare,* **1 hour 30** *minutes to cook* • **32 POINTS** *values per recipe* • **450** *calories per serving*

2 tablespoons flour
450 g (1 lb) lean stewing steak, cut into cubes
low fat cooking spray
100 g (3½ oz) cubed pancetta
10 baby onions, peeled
225 g (8 oz) carrots, peeled and cut into chunks
50 g (1¾ oz) green pitted olives in brine, drained
1 bay leaf
1 sprig of fresh rosemary
150 ml (5 fl oz) red wine
450 ml (16 fl oz) hot beef stock
salt and freshly ground black pepper
To serve
150 g (5½ oz) polenta
700 ml (1¼ pts) hot chicken stock
1 tablespoon fresh thyme leaves

❶ Preheat the oven to Gas Mark 4/180°C/fan oven 160°C. Place the flour in a shallow dish, season and coat each piece of beef. Spray a large, lidded, ovenproof casserole dish with the cooking spray and heat until hot. Add the beef in batches, cooking and turning until brown. Remove each batch to a plate before continuing.

❷ Spray the dish again and add the pancetta and onions. Cook for 3–4 minutes then return the beef to the dish with the carrots, olives, herbs, wine and stock. Stir well. Bring to the boil and cover. Place in the oven and leave to cook for 1½ hours until the beef is tender.

❸ To make the polenta, place in a pan with the stock and thyme. Bring to the boil, stirring continuously until thick.

❹ Serve the beef with the runny polenta.

granita

Granita is similar to sorbet with more of a slushy, crushed ice texture. Enjoy as a palate cleanser or as a refreshing dessert.

*Takes **10** minutes to prepare + freezing*

For the lemon version

Ⓨ ❄ *Serves **4** • **4** POINTS values per recipe*
• **95** *calories per serving*

finely grated zest of 2 lemons, plus the juice of 3
6 tablespoons caster sugar

❶ Place the lemon zest and juice and sugar in a pan and bring to the boil. Simmer for 5–6 minutes until syrupy. Pour the syrup into a measuring jug and make up to 600 ml (1 pint) with cold water.
❷ Pour into a shallow metal tray and freeze for about an hour.
❸ Every hour, remove the tray from the freezer and scrape the ice to break it up into slushy crystals. Do this for about 4 hours. Store in a freezerproof, lidded plastic box until required.

For the coffee version

Ⓨ ❄ *Serves **4** • **1** POINTS value per recipe*
• **18** *calories per serving*

2 tablespoons instant coffee
1 tablespoon caster sugar

❶ Place the coffee and sugar in a measuring jug and add a little boiling water, just enough to dissolve both. Make up to 600 ml (1 pint) with cold water.
❷ Pour into a shallow metal tray and freeze for about an hour.
❸ Every hour, remove the tray from the freezer and scrape the ice to break it up into slushy crystals for about 4 hours. Store in a freezerproof, lidded plastic box until required.

Enjoy a superb selection of simple and innovative desserts for special occasions or to share with friends and family anytime.

fennel biscuits

*Olive oil helps to keep the **POINTS** values low in these delicious biscuits flavoured with aniseed. They have a slightly crunchy outer layer with a spongy inner one, similar to soft amaretti.*

Ⓥ *Makes* **16** • *Takes* **10** *minutes to prepare,* **15** *minutes to bake* • **22½ POINTS** *values per recipe* • **84** *calories per serving*

75 ml (3 fl oz) olive oil
75 ml (3 fl oz) medium white wine
50 g (1¾ oz) golden caster sugar
125 g (4½ oz) plain flour
½ teaspoon baking powder
1 teaspoon finely grated lemon zest
1 teaspoon fennel seeds
2 teaspoons icing sugar, for dusting

❶ Preheat the oven to Gas Mark 4/180°C/fan oven 160°C. Line two baking trays with non stick baking parchment.

❷ Place the oil, wine and sugar in a bowl. Beat vigorously to combine.

❸ Sift the flour and baking powder together and fold into the sugar mixture with the lemon zest and fennel seeds. Place teaspoonfuls on the trays, spaced well apart as they will spread. Bake for 15 minutes until set (they will change a little in colour).

❹ Remove from the oven and cool on the trays for 5 minutes then transfer to a wire rack to cool completely. Dust with the icing sugar. Store in an airtight container for up to 3 days.

Variation *You could try a teaspoon of orange zest with ½ a teaspoon of cinnamon in place of the lemon and fennel, for the same **POINTS** values per serving.*

Goes well with...

*The Poached Nectarines in Wine on page 54, to serve on the side, for an extra 2 **POINTS** values per serving.*

chocolate biscuit cake

Squares of this easy refrigerator cake are great with coffee, after a meal.

Ⓥ *Makes* **20 pieces** • *Takes* **15** *minutes + setting* • **28½ POINTS** *values per recipe* • **85** *calories per serving*

75 g (2¾ oz) dark chocolate, broken into squares
200 g (7 oz) light condensed milk
110 g (4 oz) amaretti biscuits, crushed roughly
10 g (¼ oz) piece stem ginger, diced
110 g (4 oz) glacé cherries, halved

❶ Line an 900 g (2 lb) loaf tin with non stick baking parchment. Place the chocolate and condensed milk in a small pan and heat gently until melted.

❷ Place the biscuits, ginger and cherries in a large bowl. Add the melted chocolate mixture and stir until everything is well coated.

❸ Spoon into the tin, spreading out evenly. Chill for at least an hour until set, before cutting it into 10 slices and cutting each slice in half. Store in an airtight container in the fridge for up to 5 days.

Variations *If you prefer, use milk chocolate instead of the dark, for the same **POINTS** values per serving.*

*The amaretti biscuits add a slight almond flavour to this cake. If you prefer, use 150 g (5½ oz) crushed reduced fat digestive biscuits, for the same **POINTS** values per serving.*

amaretti honeyed ice cream

This home made ice cream is easy to make and yet impressive. Serve it in pretty glass dishes.

❄ *Serves* **6** *(two scoops each)* • *Takes* **10** *minutes to prepare + freezing* • **11½** *POINTS values per recipe* • **137** *calories per serving*

500 g tub reduced fat ready made custard
2 tablespoons honey
50 g (1¾ oz) amaretti biscuits, crushed roughly
6 fan wafers, to serve

❶ Mix all the ingredients together and pour into a shallow, lidded freezerproof container. Freeze for an hour and then stir well to break up the crystals that have formed around the edges.

❷ Return to the freezer and repeat every hour for the next 3 hours until smooth. Alternatively, you could churn it in an ice cream machine.

❸ Serve two scoops each with a wafer.

Serving suggestion *Affogato is ice cream served in hot espresso coffee. To make it, pour espresso coffee into a shallow cup or glass and add a scoop of the ice cream.*

Variation *For a tutti frutti version, add 60 g (2 oz) mixed dried fruit, such as raisins, sultanas, chopped glacé cherries and chopped candied peel, soaked in 3 tablespoons of orange juice for 20 minutes, instead of the biscuits, for the same POINTS values per serving.*

poached nectarines in white wine

Gently simmered fruit in wine is an Italian treat and makes the most of the country's bounteous fruit.

Ⓨ *Serves* **4** • *Takes* **15** *minutes* • **9** *POINTS values per recipe* • **157** *calories per serving*

100 ml (3½ fl oz) white wine
1 tablespoon caster sugar
1 sprig of fresh rosemary
2 pared strips of lemon peel
4 nectarines
4 x 60 g scoops of low fat vanilla ice cream,
**   to serve**

❶ Pour the wine and 50 ml (2 fl oz) of water into a medium size, lidded pan. Add the sugar, rosemary and lemon peel and bring to the boil. Cover and simmer for 5 minutes until slightly syrupy.

❷ Halve and stone the nectarines and slice into wedges. Add to the syrup, cover and put on a low heat for 5 minutes, just enough to soften the fruit. Remove from the heat and cool slightly.

❸ Remove the rosemary and lemon peel. Serve warm or cold, with a scoop of ice cream.

Tip *These nectarines can be kept covered in the fridge for up to 5 days.*

Variation *Add a vanilla pod to the wine instead of the rosemary and lemon. Simmer for 5 minutes before slitting the pod and scraping out the seeds to put back into the syrup.*

spiced apple bread pudding

Sliced spiced apples with a bread and custard topping – proper comfort eating.

Ⓨ *Serves* **6** • *Takes* **10** *minutes to prepare, plus soaking,* **20–25** *minutes to cook* • **11½** *POINTS values per recipe* • **148** *calories per serving*

low fat cooking spray
3 eating apples, peeled, cored and sliced thinly
3 tablespoons caster sugar
½ teaspoon mixed spice
110 g (4 oz) white sliced bread, crusts removed
2 eggs, beaten
300 ml (10 fl oz) skimmed milk
½ teaspoon vanilla extract

❶ Spray a 25 cm (10 inch) oval shallow ovenproof dish with the cooking spray. Place the apple slices in the base.

❷ Mix together 2 tablespoons of the sugar and the mixed spice. Sprinkle evenly over the apples. Cut the bread into triangles and arrange on top of the apples. Beat together the eggs and milk with the vanilla extract. Pour over the bread so that each triangle is coated. Cover and leave to soak for at least 30 minutes and up to 3 hours (if leaving for more than 30 minutes, refrigerate).

❸ Preheat the oven to Gas Mark 5/190°C/fan oven 170°C. Place the pudding on a baking tray, sprinkle with the remaining sugar and bake for 20–25 minutes until golden.

Tip *The milk curdles slightly but it still tastes great.*

roasted stuffed peaches

Ensure the fruit is ripe so that the roasted peaches will be sweet and juicy.

Ⓥ Serves **4** • Takes **10** minutes to prepare, **20** minutes to cook • **7 POINTS** values per recipe
• **97** calories per serving

2 **peaches**
150 ml (5 fl oz) orange juice
60 g (2 oz) ricotta cheese
1 tablespoon icing sugar, sifted
½ teaspoon vanilla extract
25 g (1 oz) amaretti biscuits, crushed roughly

❶ Preheat the oven to Gas Mark 5/190°C/fan oven 170°C. Halve and stone the peaches and place cut side up in a snug fitting ovenproof dish. Pour the orange juice into the dish so that the peaches sit in the juice.

❷ Beat together the ricotta cheese, icing sugar and vanilla extract. Divide the mixture between the holes in the peaches. Scatter over the amaretti biscuits and bake for 20 minutes until softened. Serve one peach half each with some of the juice from the dish.

Tip If you are not keen on amaretti biscuits, use 40 g (1½ oz) reduced fat crushed digestive biscuits instead, for a **POINTS** value of 2½ per serving.

Variation You can use ripe nectarines or plums instead of the peaches. The **POINTS** values will remain the same.

strawberry and vanilla panna cotta

Serves **4** • Takes **10** minutes to prepare + soaking + cooling • **12½ POINTS** values per recipe
• **162** calories per serving

4 gelatine leaves
225 g (8 oz) strawberries, hulled and sliced
2 tablespoons caster sugar
400 ml (14 fl oz) skimmed milk
1 vanilla pod, slit lengthways
200 ml (7 fl oz) reduced fat single cream
1 teaspoon vanilla extract

❶ Cut the gelatine leaves into strips, place in a bowl and just cover with cold water. Soak for 5 minutes, then drain and set aside.

❷ Place the strawberries in a small pan with 4 tablespoons of water and 2 teaspoons of the sugar. Simmer gently for 3 minutes just to soften the strawberries. Set aside to cool.

❸ Place the milk, remaining sugar and vanilla pod in a separate small pan and bring to the boil, watching carefully so that it doesn't boil over. Remove from the heat and scrape out the seeds from the vanilla pod, returning them to the milk. Add the gelatine and stir to dissolve. If it doesn't completely dissolve, return to the heat and warm gently until dissolved. Stir in the cream and vanilla extract.

❹ Pour the mixture into four individual pudding basins or 150 ml (5 fl oz) ramekins and chill for at least 2 hours. To serve, dip the basins or ramekins into warm water to loosen then invert a small serving plate over the top and turn over to tip out. Serve with the poached strawberries spooned over the top.

Goes well after...

The Braised Sea Bass with Fresh Tomato Sauce on page 34, for a summer supper party as a make ahead dessert, for an extra 4 **POINTS** values per serving.

zabaglione with raspberries

This warming mousse should be served in small glasses as it is very rich.

Ⓨ Serves **4** • Takes **15** minutes • **12** *POINTS* values per recipe • **220** calories per serving

4 **egg yolks**
75 g (2¾ oz) caster sugar
100 ml (3½ fl oz) Marsala wine or sweet sherry
150 g (5½ oz) **raspberries**

❶ Place the egg yolks, sugar and Marsala or sherry in a large bowl (the mixture will more than double in volume). Place the bowl over a pan of gently simmering water. Whisk the mixture until it is pale and very thick – it is easiest to do this with an electric whisk. It may take as long as 10 minutes.
❷ Pour the warm foam into four small wine or shot glasses.
❸ Drop the raspberries into the foam and serve immediately.

Serving suggestion *Serve with two amaretti biscuits each, for an extra ½ POINTS value per serving.*

Goes well after...

The Whole Roasted Chicken with Garlic and Lemon on page 46, for 5 POINTS values per serving.

strawberry and chocolate tiramisu

Ⓨ Serves **4** • Takes **10** minutes to prepare + chilling • **16** *POINTS* values per recipe • **192** calories per serving

225 g (8 oz) **strawberries**, hulled
3 teaspoons icing sugar
75 g (2¾ oz) light mascarpone
75 g (2¾ oz) 0% fat Greek yogurt
1 teaspoon vanilla extract
75 g (2¾ oz) sponge fingers, broken in two
15g (½ oz) dark chocolate, grated

❶ Place half the strawberries in a food processor or blender. Blend until smooth. Add 1 teaspoon of the sugar. Blend again to make a coulis. Slice the remaining strawberries and set aside.
❷ Lay out four small glass serving dishes. Beat together the mascarpone, yogurt, vanilla extract and remaining sugar.
❸ Reserving a couple of strawberry slices for decoration, add half the strawberries to the dishes and drizzle over a little of the coulis. Add half of the broken fingers, then repeat the layers. Top with the mascarpone mixture, sprinkle over the chocolate and decorate with the remaining strawberry slices. Chill for at least 10 minutes or for as long as 2 hours.

orange and almond cake

This fantastically moist cake keeps really well - in fact the flavour improves a day or so after baking.

Ⓨ *Serves* **10** • *Takes* **20** *minutes to prepare +* **1 hour** *cooking,* **50** *minutes to bake* • **38½ POINTS** *values per recipe* • **135** *calories per serving*

2 oranges, **scrubbed and left unpeeled**
low fat cooking spray
1 teaspoon baking powder
4 eggs
2 egg whites
200 g (7 oz) light brown sugar
175 g (6 oz) ground almonds
2 tablespoons dried breadcrumbs
2 tablespoons runny honey

❶ Place the whole oranges in a large pan and cover with cold water. Bring to the boil and simmer for 30 minutes. Drain and cover again with cold water. Bring to the boil and simmer for another 30 minutes. Drain and cool in cold water.

❷ Spray a 20 cm (8 inch) springform tin with the cooking spray. Base line with non stick baking parchment.

❸ When the oranges are cold enough to handle, quarter, remove any pips and place in a blender. Blitz until smooth. Add the baking powder and blend again. Preheat the oven to Gas Mark 4/180°C/fan oven 170°C.

❹ Place the eggs and egg whites in a large bowl with the sugar and whisk with an electric whisk until pale and frothy. You do not need to whisk until thick and creamy. Stir in the ground almonds and breadcrumbs, then the orange mixture.

❺ Pour the batter into the cake tin and bake for 50 minutes. Test if it is cooked by inserting a skewer in the middle of the cake, which should come out clean. While still hot, drizzle over the honey and leave to cool in the tin.

Tip *The cake should be covered and stored in the fridge where it can be kept for up to 3 days.*

mascarpone cheesecake with Marsala sultanas

Marsala and brown sugar give this baked cheesecake a lovely treacle flavour. Bake it ahead of time for a supper party.

Ⓨ *Serves* **10** • *Takes* **10** *minutes to prepare,* **40–50** *minutes to bake* • **46½** *POINTS values per recipe* • **214** *calories per serving*

50 g (1¾ oz) sultanas
3 tablespoons Marsala wine or brandy
25 g (1 oz) low fat polyunsaturated margarine
125 g (4½ oz) reduced fat ginger snaps, crushed
250 g tub light mascarpone
300 g (10½ oz) virtually fat free fromage frais
4 tablespoons light brown sugar
2 eggs, beaten
finely grated zest of 1 orange

❶ Preheat the oven to Gas Mark 4/180°C/fan oven 160°C. Base line a 20 cm (8 inch) springform tin with non stick baking parchment. Place the sultanas in a small pan with the Marsala or brandy and heat gently for 3 minutes. Remove from the heat.

❷ Melt the margarine in a large pan, remove from the heat and stir in the crushed biscuits. Press the mixture into the base of the tin. Chill until required.

❸ In a large bowl, use an electric whisk to beat together the mascarpone and fromage frais until smooth then beat in the sugar and eggs. Stir in the cooled sultana mixture and orange zest. Pour over the base and bake for 40–50 minutes until golden and almost set with just a slight wobble in the middle. Remove from the oven and leave to cool in the tin.

Tip *Cover the cheesecake and it will keep in the fridge for 3–4 days.*

baked orange and candied peel ricotta puddings

These individual puddings have a light texture and a great orange flavour.

Ⓨ *Serves* **4** • *Takes* **10** *minutes to prepare,* **15** *minutes to bake* • **18½** *POINTS values per recipe* • **224** *calories per serving*

low fat cooking spray
250 g tub ricotta cheese
2 eggs, beaten
½ teaspoon vanilla extract
2 tablespoons caster sugar
½ teaspoon cinnamon
30 g (1¼ oz) candied peel, chopped
finely grated zest of ½ an orange, plus long
     zested strips, to decorate

❶ Spray four mini pudding basins or four 150 ml (5 fl oz) ramekins with the cooking spray and base line with non stick baking parchment.

❷ Use an electric whisk to beat together the ricotta cheese, eggs, vanilla and sugar until smooth. Stir in the cinnamon and candied peel with the orange zest. Spoon the mixture into the basins and place in a shallow baking tin. Bake for 15 minutes until the tops are firm but not brown.

❸ To serve, run a round ended knife around the edge to loosen and invert on to small serving plates. Decorate with the orange zest strips. Serve warm or cold.

Tip *These puddings will keep in the fridge for up to 2 days and can be reheated in the microwave for 1 minute or served cold.*